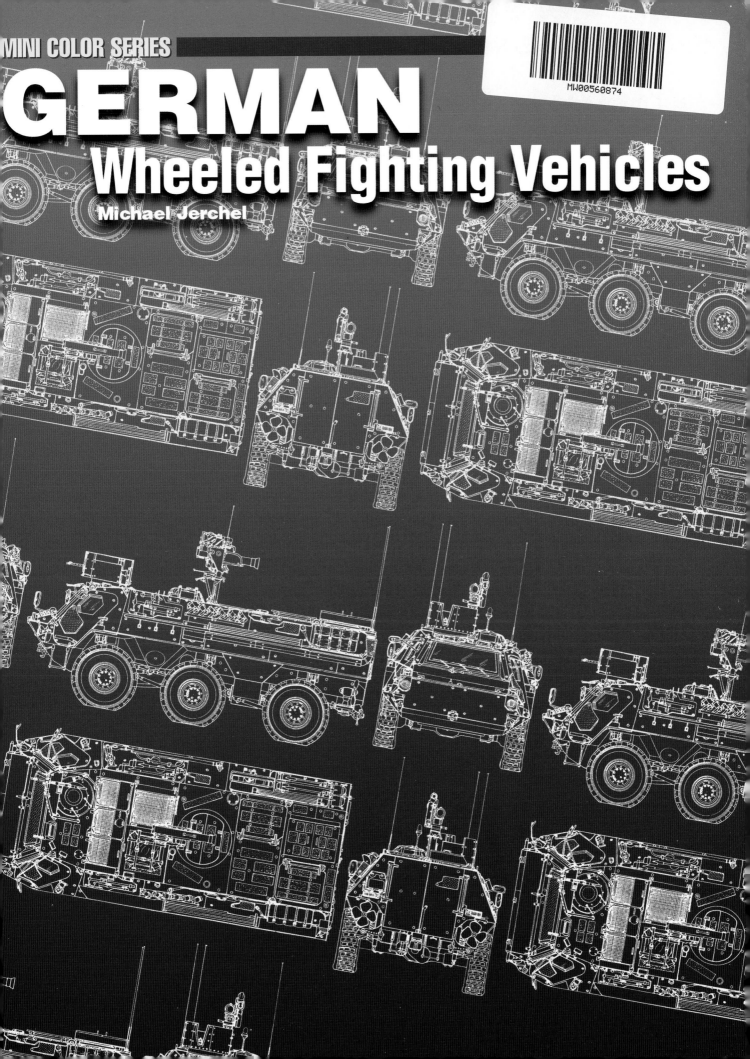

MINI COLOR SERIES

GERMAN
Wheeled Fighting Vehicles

Michael Jerchel

Acknowledgements

Special thanks are due to Mrs. Baumgart of MaK, Mr. Jedlhauser of Henschel Wehrtechnik, Mr. Kerwin of Krauss Maffei-Wegmann, Lt. Col. Hunte of Heeresamt, the employees of the Fachmedienzentrale der Panzertruppenschule, Christopher Foss, Jürgen Plate, Andreas Kirchhoff, Sabine Rotter, Carl Schulze, Uwe Schnellbacher, Uwe Remmers, and Volkmar Roesner for providing helpful information and additional photographs.

All photos by Michael Jerchel unless otherwise stated.

In 1962, a long series of trials and studies was launched by the Bundesamt für Wehrtechnik und Beschaffung, BWB (Federal Office of Military Technology and Procurement) to establish the basic principles of the future policy for the next generation of tactical trucks and wheeled armored fighting vehicles. In 1964 the BWB recognized that those vehicles should share a high degree of commonality — to be achieved wherever possible — and the usage of commercial components, emphasizing above all the importance of standardization for a vast range of tactical trucks and the required multi-role wheeled armored vehicles.

For the development program, a joint project office (Gemeinschaft-Büro, or GB), which included the five largest truck building companies of that time (Büssing, Henschel, MAN and Klöckner-Humbold-Deutz) was formed competing against Daimler Benz (DB). The first manufacturer's trials began in 1967, and in April 1968 the comparative trials of each manufacturer's prototype of the Transportpanzer 1 (6 x 6), Transportpanzer 2 (4 x 4), and the Spähpanzer 2 (8 x 8) were conducted at the WTD 41 proving ground in Trier. In 1969 the development program was changed slightly when the requirement for the Transportpanzer 2 (4 x 4) was dropped. The Transportpanzer 1 (6 x 6) was to have a payload of 2 tonnes (2.25 tons) and a capability of transporting ten soldiers.

Concerning the Spähpanzer (8 x 8), after careful examination of the results of the comparative trials, and under certain pressure to replace the outdated M41 and Hotchkiss light reconnaissance tanks, the prototype developed by DB was selected for further development in 1969. In December 1973, after finding that each specified requirement had been satisfied and often exceeded, the German Ministry of Defense (BMVg) approved the adoption into service of the now officially designated Spähpanzer 2 Luchs (Lynx). Series production started in 1975 at Thyssen Henschel in Kassel (now Henschel Wehrtechnik), under license of the chosen main contractor, DB, and in 1977 the last of the 408 vehicles ordered was delivered to the Bundeswehr.

The SpPz 2 is lightly armored, but this is sufficient to protect against shrapnel and small arms fire and against hits up to 20 mm over the frontal arc. It operates at a very low noise level and is fully amphibious. Two propellers installed at the rear of the vehicle are used for propulsion in the water. The maximum speed achievable on the road is 90 km/h (56 mph) and 10 km/h (6.2 mph) in the water. The combat weight is around 19,500 kg (42,900 lb.). The main armament consists of a 20 mm Rheinmetall Rh 202 cannon, and a 7.62 mm MG 3 machine gun is provided as a secondary weapon. One of the special features of the SpPz 2 is the provision for a rearward driver, enabling the Luchs to be driven at the same speed in either direction. An all-wheel steering option can be used to achieve a speed up to 30 km/h (19 mph).

The installation of a new generation of radio beginning in 1985, the SEM 80/90, led to the vehicle's new designation — SpPz 2 Luchs A1. After further modernization, which included the installation of a thermal sight and the deletion of the searchlight, the vehicle became known as the SpPz 2 Luchs A2. Due to the modernization, the vehicle gained a lot of weight, which unfortunately affected its center of gravity as well. Special pontoons were developed to be attached to the vehicle's sides, but they proved to be impractical. However, due to the modifications, the vehicle is no longer suited for peacetime amphibious operations.

The SpPz Luchs A2 is also in use with the German contingent of the Stabilization Force (SFOR) in Bosnia and Herzegovina, where a number of vehicles were recently upgraded with a gyrocompass, an additional special antenna and the installation of the global positioning system (GPS), all fitted to the upper rear deck.

Following military demands made in 1985 for an airportable light reconnaissance vehicle, a VBL (Véhicule Blindé Léger, or light armored vehicle) offered by MaK and Panhard was tested in the late eighties against the Zobel built by GST. The Zobel was favored by BWB and Heeresamt to become the platform for the definition phase of the 4 x 4 light reconnaissance vehicle program, for which DAF/Wegmann was chosen to build four pre-series vehicles, now known as the Fennek (Desert Fox). The first vehicle was delivered in November 1996, two of which were tested by the Royal Netherlands Army, and two by Bundeswehr. The vehicle offers all-around protection from small arms fire (7.62 mm AP) and shrapnel. Add-on armor technology would make it possible to enhance this protection as needed. The crew compartment is protected from anti-personnel mines, the IR signature has been considerably reduced due to a special exhaust ducting, and the engine compartment is fitted with a fire extinguishing and warning system, which can be activated automatically or manually.

The Fennek, which has a built-in NBC protection system, is operated by a crew of three. The major reconnaissance components are the tactical command and control system (TCCS), and a sensor head on an extendible mast. The sensor head, which can be raised to a height of 1.5 meters (1.7 yards) above the vehicle's roof, is controlled in both azimuth and elevation. The sensor head contains a thermal imager, a CCD day vision camera and a laser rangefinder. If required, the sensor head can be put on a tripod up to 40 meters (44 yards) away from the vehicle and operated by remote control. The built-in global positioning system (GPS) permits highly accurate target coordinate determinations (10 m CEP). For self-defense, the Fennek is armed with a 40 mm automatic grenade launcher in an electrically controlled gun mount, which is operated from inside the vehicle. Optionally, a 7.62 mm or a .50 caliber machine gun can be fitted.

The powerpack of the Fennek develops 177 kW (241 PS), which allows a maximum speed of 115 km/h (71 mph) on roads. The vehicle has a combat weight of 9,700 kg (21,340 lb.) and a range of 860 km (534 miles) on roads and 400 km (248 miles) cross-country. The turning radius is 6.3 meters (7 yards). According to plans, the 336 Fennek yet to be built will replace the SpPz 2 Luchs A2 in the near future.

In 1970 Daimler Benz also won the competition for the Transportpanzer (6 x 6). With production priority given to the Spähpanzer (SpPz) 2, BWB, the office of procurement and development, placed an order for 996 Transportpanzer 1 Fuchs (Fox) in 1977. The series production began in 1979 at Thyssen Henschel in Kassel under license of DB. The first vehicle was handed over officially to Bundeswehr in December 1979, and the last of the original order was delivered in late 1986.

The TPz-1 Fuchs of the standard version was fitted with a Rüstsatz, i.e., installation kit. This could either be the Combat Engineer installation kit, MILAN ATGW carrier kit, Command and Control vehicle installation kit for air defense and engineer units, or the Ambulance kit. With the SEM 80/90 installed, these vehicles are known as the TPz-1 Fuchs A4. The Fuchs is fully amphibious and has two Schottel rudder propellers installed at the rear of the vehicle, giving it a maximum speed of 10.5 km/h (6.5 mph) in the water.

A special electronic warfare version known as the TPz-1 A1 Hummel (Bumble Bee) was developed. It lacks amphibious capability and therefore has no trim vane and no propellers installed. A small number were used by the Allied forces during Operation "Desert Storm", and 18 vehicles are also in service with the Royal Netherlands Army.

The command/control and communication version (including the RASIT radar carrier) is known as the TPz-1 A2, and is designated as TPz-1 A5 when the SEM 80/90 radios are fitted.

The NBC reconnaissance version, which entered service in 1988, is also known as the NBC-Fox. It is designated as ABC-Spürpanzer TPz-1 Fuchs A3. With SEM 80/90 radios fitted, its designation is TPz-1 Fuchs ABC A6. During Operation "Desert Storm", eight were delivered from Bundeswehr stocks to Israel, four went to Turkey, 11 to the United Kingdom and 60 to the US Army (latter designated the M93 NBCRS).

The Transportpanzer 1 Fuchs A4 has a crew of two and can carry up to 10 soldiers, all seated in the rear compartment. The vehicle is powered by a V-8 cylinder, liquid-cooled Daimler Benz OM 402A diesel engine, which can develop 320 PS. This provides the TPz-1, with a combat weight of 17,000 kg (37,400 lb.), a maximum speed of 105 km/h (65 mph) on the road.

For service with SFOR in Bosnia and Herzegovina, most of the TPz-1 (all versions) in use there were modified with screw-on additional armor and a better armored windscreen. At a later stage, the vehicles were fitted with extra armor plates around the machine gun station.

A development program is currently underway, under the designation GTK, to eventually replace the Transportpanzer 1.

For enhanced protection, many of the tactical trucks in service with the German contingent of IFOR (and later SFOR) in Croatia and Bosnia were fitted with additional armor plates, known as modular armor. This includes the 2-ton, 5-ton, 7-ton, 10-ton and 15-ton trucks, as well as the Elefant tank transporter. Those trucks received armor protection around the machine gun position as well. Additional armor was also fitted to the 3/4-ton 4 x 4 Wolf utility vehicle, which unfortunately reduces the seat capacity from four to two.

A number of Mercedes Benz 3/4 ton Wolf utility vehicles (250 GD) were fitted with armor plates for service with SFOR in the former Yugoslavia. Because of the armor, the seating capacity is reduced to two. This vehicle is seen during a patrol near Sarajevo in March 1997.

A fully armored version of the Wolf (290 GD) in service with the German contingent of SFOR was purchased by the Bundeswehr from stocks of the German border patrol. The one shown here is in service with the German military police on patrol in Dobrinia near Sarajevo airport in early 1997.

The fully armored Wolf (290 GD), which is equipped with an air conditioner and SEM 25/35 radios, provides space for four persons. The one seen here is making its way through the German-French camp in Railovac, near Sarajevo, in August 1998.

4

This 2-ton Unimog tactical truck of Luftlandebrigade 26 (Airborne Brigade 26) has been fitted with improvised protection for use as an evacuation vehicle. Perhaps it will be seen in some future international peacekeeping operation.

Another type of improvised protection appears on a 2-ton tactical truck of Luftlandebrigade 26, which is to be used as an evacuation vehicle for threatened civilians. The improvised protection consists of sandbags that have even been placed inside the cab behind the windscreen.

Most of the 2-ton Unimogs used by the Bundeswehr in Bosnia have been fitted with modular armor on the cab and a bulletproof windscreen. The two vehicles shown are part of the explosive ordnance disposal (EOD) unit. They were photographed at Rajlovac in early 1997.

5

An armored cab was developed by MAN and Krauss Maffei to be fitted to any of the 5-, 7- or 10-ton MAN tactical trucks in current service. This one is an early prototype, which, interestingly, lacks a hatch in the roof. The cab can be fitted with an NBC protective system. (Sabine Rotter)

For the German contingent of IFOR in Croatia and later SFOR in Bosnia, the cabs of the MAN tactical trucks were also fitted with additional armor plating (modular armor) around the frontal area and sides. A bulletproof windscreen and an air conditioner were also added. This 5-ton truck, which is a veteran of the IFOR mission (as indicated by the tactical markings), now serves with SFOR in Rajlovac.

The MG 3 machine gun position was also fitted with armor plates at the front and on the sides. The latter can be folded down when not in use, as seen here on a MAN 5-ton tactical truck.

This 7-ton MAN 6 x 6 tactical truck with armored cab, seen at the German-French camp in Rajlovac in early 1997, bears the name "Mad Max II".

A 10-ton MAN 8 x 8 tactical truck with armored cab and 1-ton crane tows a 10-ton trailer. The truck is powered by a V-8 cylinder diesel engine, which can produce 320 PS. While the vehicle sports the regular camouflage pattern consisting of green (RAL 6031), brown (RAL 8027) and black (RAL 9021), the armor plates on the cab remain plain green (RAL 6031).

The 110 mm light artillery rocket system LARS 2 is based on the chassis of the 7-ton MAN 6 x 6 tactical truck. It consists of two packs with 18 barrels.

The Artillerie Raketenwerfer 110 SF2, as the LARS 2 is called by the Federal German Army, is used by the rocket artillery battalions of the division. It was supplemented by the MLRS in the late 1980s. A 7.62 mm MG 3 is fitted on the cab for air defense purposes.

The 36 rockets of the LARS 2 can be fired singly, in a partial ripple or in one volley. A full ripple can be fired in 17.5 seconds. The normal range for the 110 mm rocket is between 6,000 and 14,000 meters (6,558 and 15,300 yards). Fire control is maintained by the FERA radar, which is based on a 5-ton MAN tactical truck.

The wide variety of payloads includes DM-15 smoke, DM-11 and DM-21 fragmentation, DM-711 AT-2 mines, and DM-39 radar target. The latter is fitted with a radar reflector and is used as the pilot shot for the FERA fire control radar, as seen here. (Volkmar Rösner)

The FlaRakRad (FFR) Roland (air defense system, wheeled) is shelter-mounted and carried by a 15-ton 8 x 8 tactical truck. A FFR is seen here with the lock-on and surveillance radar in operation. The launchers are in firing position. Barely visible are the two large flaps below the two launcher arms, which cover the reload magazines, containing four missile containers each. The reloading sequence is conducted within 10 seconds.

In this rear view, only the surveillance radar is in operation. The launchers are in fold-down position.

The shelter of the FFR Roland can be deployed while separated from the truck. It is fitted with an auxiliary power unit and an NBC protection system.

To deploy the shelter separately from the truck, the crew of the FFR Roland has to manually carry out the load/unload operation with the use of four large jacks. There are 60 FFR Roland in service with the German Air Force (Luftwaffe), with another 27 systems operated by German crews. They provide air defense for Allied air bases.

A further 20 vehicles are in service with the German Navy, as is depicted here. The cab of the 15-ton 8 x 8 tactical truck can be tilted forward, allowing easy access to the engine compartment.

A turret with a quadruple launcher was offered by Euromissile, but it has not entered service until now. (Euromissile)

The FGR weapon control system/radar is a mobile air defense center with integrated TRM-L sensor. It is used for air situation sensing and airspace observation, as well as mission planning for and control of air defense weapons against low- and intermediate-level hostile aircraft and missiles. The radar of this FGR is shown here in traveling position.

During an operation, up to ten FFR Roland systems can be connected to one FGR, which is seen here with its 2 D C-band radar in operation. This system is based on the same chassis as the FFR, the 15-ton MAN 8 x 8 tactical truck.

The EPLA (Elevierbare Kampfplattform, i.e., elevating platform), was developed by Krauss Maffei in cooperation with MBB, MAN and Euromissile. The platform can be operated either by one man seated inside of it or by remote control. It is based on a MAN 8 x 8 Kat. A1 truck. The EPLA is not in service with Bundeswehr, but a number of customers have shown an interest.

An SLT 50-3 Elefant tank transporter, with modular armor fitted around the cab, is seen here sitting on a ramp at the German-French camp in Rajlovac in August 1998.

The production of the Transportpanzer 1 Fuchs (Fox) began at Thyssen Henschel (now Henschel Wehrtechnik) in 1979. This photo shows the underside of the vehicle to good advantage. (Thyssen Henschel)

The SLT 50-3 has a turbo-charged V-12 diesel engine, which can develop 540 kW (735 PS) at 2,100 rpm, allowing a maximum speed of 65 km/h 40 mph (empty, 40 km/h [25 mph] with a load of 52 tonnes [56 tons]). The Elefant was designed to carry loads up to the MLC 60 class. The vehicle depicted here is the up-armored version in service in Bosnia. It has been named "Diana" by its crew.

The Transportpanzer 1 Fuchs is powered by a liquid-cooled V-8 cylinder Mercedes Benz OM 402A diesel engine, developing 320 PS at 2,500 rpm. Due to quick disconnect couplings, it requires only about ten minutes time to pull out the engine pack.

The engine compartment is situated between the driver's/commander's compartment and the rear cargo/passenger area. It is equipped with an automatic fire-extinguishing system. There is a small crawlway between the forward and rear compartments.

A TPz-1 ambulance is seen following its return from deployment with the German UN contingent in Somalia at Emden harbor in March 1994. The photo shows to advantage the LS7FS power-assisted circulating ball-and-nut steering of both forward axles. The turning radius measures 17 meters (18.5 yards) in diameter.

The Rüstsatz SAN (ambulance installation kit) allows the transportation of up to four stretchers or four seated persons, plus medical personnel. There is no smoke mortar array fitted on this version.

A rather rare TPz-1 A4 in its standard configuration without any Rüstsatz (installation kit). It is seen at Trier WTD 41 proving grounds, where it was perhaps used in conjunction with the development of additional armor for service in Bosnia. The TPz-1 is fully amphibious, and achieves a maximum speed of over 10 km/h (6 mph) in the water by using the two rudder propellers installed at the rear of the vehicle. The exhaust pipe runs along the left side of the vehicle. The device attached to the upper rear end of the pipe is normally found only on up-armored vehicles.

For service in Bosnia among SFOR, with a considerably increased threat, all TPz-1 ambulances were fitted with additional armor plates around the body and on the roof. The TPz-1 A4 SAN vehicles in Bosnia are under the command of the German-French Field Hospital. They provide medical support to patrols. The vehicle seen here was photographed during a patrol on Mount Igman, near Sarajevo, in early 1997.

The same TPz-1 A4 SAN, named "König Ludwig" by the crew in honor of the famous king of Bavaria. The red and white warning plates are required by German traffic law since the vehicles are extended in their width due to the additional armor. This is an easy recognition feature of an up-armored variant.

A Transportpanzer 1 Fuchs A4 with Rüstsatz MILAN ATGW, the anti-tank guided weapon. The post for fitting the MILAN is visible behind the vehicle commander manning the machine gun. The first two axles of the TPz-1 are steerable. The three Mercedes Benz Type 7 axles have planetary gearing in the hubs. Longitudinal and lateral differential locks can be engaged during movement. Suspension is provided by helical springs and double-acting hydraulic shock absorbers.

The commander of this TPz-1 A4, which is fitted with a MILAN kit, aims the 7.62 mm MG 3 A1 machine gun at an aerial target during an exercise in Bergen. The windshield glass, which is 90 mm thick, can also be protected by swing-down armor plates at the front. The tactical markings and the license plates are toned down with mud.

Nowadays large-scale exercises are replaced mostly by simulations. In this case, a TPz-1 A4 with a MILAN kit simulates a tank, as denoted by the yellow triangles that were carried during Reforger 1991 exercise "Certain Shield". Quite noticeably, the camouflaged vehicle still carries the old-style large cross, the German national insignia. The tactical number "622" is all black. Note the rudder propeller at the vehicle's rear. Used in the amphibious role, the pair would swing around. Reflectors are attached to the propeller mounting struts.

The mount for the MILAN ATGM launcher is attached to a cupola with a split hatch, which replaces the cover plate in use with other versions of the TPz-1. The small mast to the right is the base for the warning light (disco light). An additional machine gun mount can be seen at the rear of the vehicle.

This photo shows the rear compartment of the MILAN version of the TPz-1. It has three bulletproof windows, and there are two hatches in the roof, measuring 80 x 60 cm (31.5 x 24 inches). All doors and hatches are sealed with rubber profiles to ensure secure amphibious operations and NBC protection.

An all-white TPz-1 A4 with a MILAN kit at a depot in Garlstedt after its return from Somalia in early 1994. It was used by mountain troops during the German participation there. Only the rubber caps on the smoke mortars remain black in color; the rest of the vehicle was painted white. Of note is the position of the UN marking on the roof.

This all-white TPz-1 A4 is fitted with a MILAN kit and wears UN markings, as used in Somalia. Quite interestingly, empty ammunition boxes have been filled with sand and fitted as additional protection around the ventral hatch.

An early example of an up-armored TPz-1 A4 with a MILAN kit, which is in service with the German contingent of the Implementation Force (IFOR) in Croatia. The vehicle has been named 'Else" by the crew. (Carl Schulze)

An up-armored TPz-1 A4 fitted with a MILAN kit patrols in Dobrinia near Sarajevo airport in early 1997. For some unknown reason, the code number of the famous fictitious starship Enterprise has been applied to the right rear door.

This up-armored TPz-1 A4 with MILAN kit bears the name of an American comic character. It is seen here on Mount Igman during a patrol in early 1997.

This up-armored TPz-1 A4 with MILAN kit is on patrol in Dobrinja in April 1997. A small windshield was attached in front of the hatch used by the patrol commander.

This TPz-1 Fuchs A4 with MILAN kit is seen in position as a mobile checkpoint during a patrol near Hadjici in April 1997. The vehicle commander keeps the 7.62 mm MG 3 A1 machine gun ready and listens to the intercom. One of the recognition features of the up-armored variant is the license plate on the bow being offset from the vehicle's centerline.

A patrol of two TPz-1 A4 and a French VBL, led by a TPz-1 A4 fitted with a MILAN kit, at Dobrinia. The patrol commander standing in the ventral position with the split hatches points at a suspicious vehicle.

1/35 Up-armored Transportpanzer 1 Fuchs A4 (Rüstsatz MILAN)

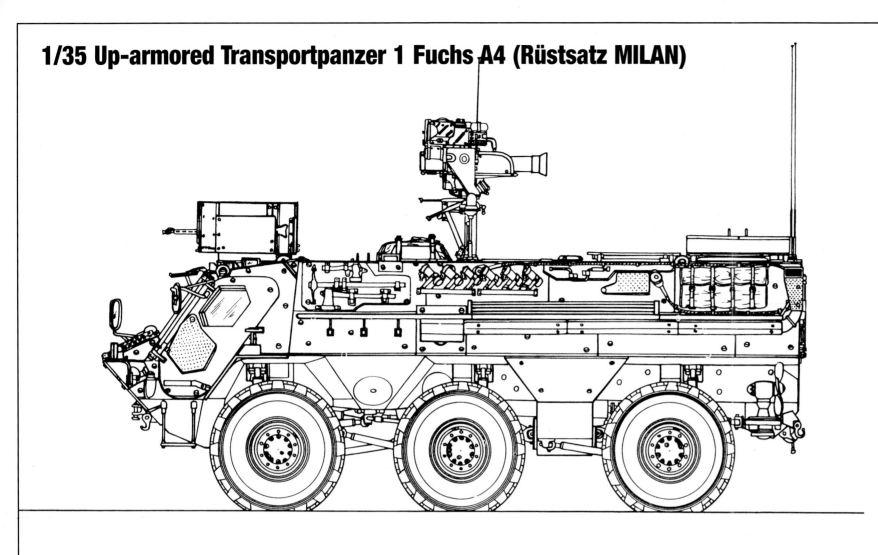

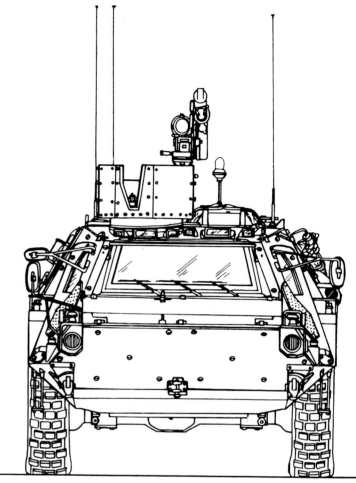

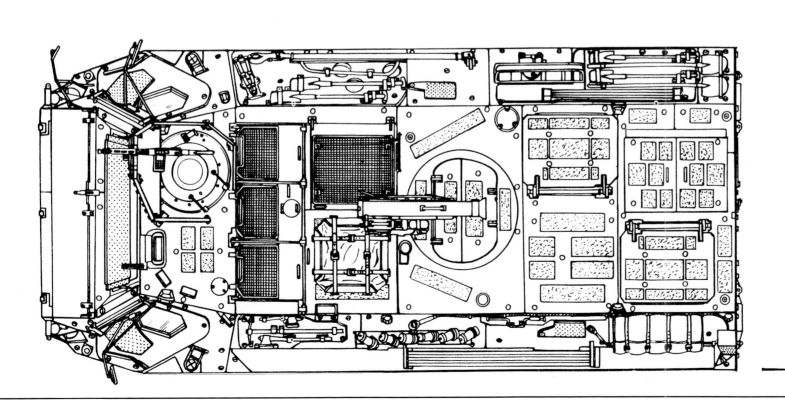

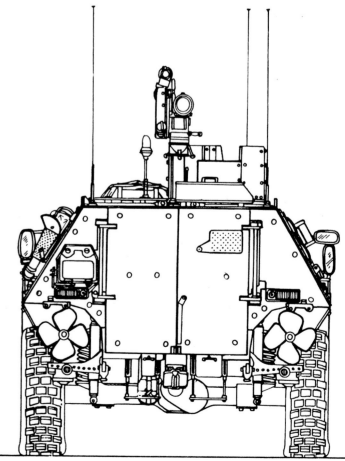

An up-armored TPz-1 A4 with MILAN kit patrols near Sarajevo in August 1998. For enhanced protection, and as a standard item, the machine gun position received armor protection very similar to that of the MAN series of tactical trucks.

The crew of this TPz-1 A4, which is fitted with a MILAN installation kit, provides maintenance service at Rajlovac camp in August 1998. The measured temperature was 70 degrees C (158 degrees F) in the sunlight!

A snow white TPz-1 Fuchs A4 with MILAN kit belonging to the Bundeswehr in service with SFOR in August 1998. It was taken from stocks of the former UN vehicles that served so well in Somalia. It is neither up-armored nor does it have the armor plates around the machine gun mount.

A Transportpanzer 1 Fuchs A4 with Rüstsatz Pioniergruppenfahrzeug, i.e., combat engineers installation kit. This version can be recognized by the two large circular containers on the roof above the rear compartment. This TPz-1 A4 is seen at high speed during an exercise at Bergen-Hohne in 1988. When traveling on roads, the TPz-1 achieves a maximum speed of 105 km/h (65 mph).

A TPz-1 A4 of Panzerpionierkompanie 340 (Combat Engineer Company 340), a brigade level unit of Panzerbrigade 34 of the 12th (GE) Panzerdivision, with the full set of tools attached to the vehicle's side. The MLC marking, with a small letter "c" on top of the gray "20", denotes a vehicle that would normally tow a 1.5-tonne (1.75-ton) trailer.

This TPz-1 A4 of Panzerpionierkompanie 340, which is passing a Marder 1 A1 MICV, provides support to a Panzergrenadier company during an exercise in Bergen. It has the early-type tires with the distinctive tread pattern.

The hinged armored covers of this combat engineer version TPz-1 A4 of Panzerpionierkompanie 10, 1st (GE) Panzerdivision are seen here in the closed position.

The view looking in a forward direction over the roof of a combat engineer version TPz-1 A4. An additional machine gun mount and hatch were installed in the ventral circular cover of this version. One of the two circular containers can be seen in foreground.

This photo shows a TPz-1 A4 of Panzerpionierkompanie 10 during an exercise in Holzminden in 1991. The device with the white cross at the rear of the vehicle is an orientation aid for vehicles following it during blacked-out night marches.

The combat engineer version TPz-1 A4 is fully amphibious. Its maximum speed in the water is 10.5 km/h (6.5 mph). The two circular containers, which differ in size, are clearly visible on the roof.

A look into the rear compartment of the combat engineer version of a TPz-1 A4, which measures 3.20 m x 1.34 m x 1.25 m (10.5 ft. x 4.5 ft x 4 ft). It is prepared to take up to ten soldiers. There are two large hatches located in the roof.

The rearmost of the two circular containers of a combat engineer TPz-1 A4, in which concertina wire is stored. The forward circular container, which is slightly smaller, is filled with wooden pegs, but it could also be used to store concertina wire or explosive charges. The cover is held in place by a simple wing nut.

This plain olive green (RAL 60140) combat engineer TPz-1 A4 is marked as a tank by a yellow triangle during its participation in the Reforger 1991 exercise "Certain Shield".

With a 1.5-tonne (1.75-ton) trailer in tow, this TPz-1 A4 combat engineer vehicle is seen during a recent exercise at the German Armor School in Munster.

Painted entirely in white, this TPz-1 A4 combat engineer vehicle was photographed in Garlstedt after returning from the UN mission in Somalia in 1994.

An up-armored TPz-1 Fuchs A4 standing next to a Spähpanzer 2 A2 Luchs prepares to go out on patrol around Sarajevo in early 1997. The main objective of such a patrol is to make a show of force.

A heavily camouflaged TPz-1 A4 combat engineer vehicle of Pionierbrigade 20 provides support during a recent exercise held near Flensburg. The Leopard 2 A4 seen in background has just fired its gunfire simulator, also known as a Hoffman device.

The latest feature to be added to the up-armored TPz-1 A4 as a standard item is the armored machine gun position. This combat engineer version TPz-1 A4 is shown patrolling around Sarajevo in August 1998.

An up-armored combat engineer TPz-1 A4, together with a Spähpanzer 2 Luchs A2, on patrol at Dobrinia in August 1998. The area around Dobrinia has been cleared of mines, and many refugees have now returned to their homes.

A combat engineer version of an up-armored TPz-1 A4 on patrol in Dobrinia near Sarajevo airport in April 1997. The vehicle wears full SFOR and coalition markings, carries the name "Lady II". The tactical markings denote a vehicle of 4th company of Gepanzerter Einsatzverband, or armored task force.

The command and control vehicle equipped with the newer SEM 80/90 radios is known as the Transportpanzer 1 Fuchs A4. It is used in this form by engineer and armored reconnaissance units. Shown here is an engineer platoon leader's vehicle during an exercise in Bergen in 1991.

Soldiers of a patrol, whose radio call-sign is "Tiger 2/5", pose in front of their TPz-1 A4 combat engineer vehicle. The G 36 automatic rifle they carry is the replacement for the G 3 rifle.

The TPz 1 A4 Führung/Funk, the command and control variant, is also fully amphibious. With it trim vane erected and Schottel propellers swung around and running, this one drives into the river Weser at high speed to gain momentum during an exercise in 1988.

The command and control vehicle is simply known as the Transportpanzer 1 Fuchs once the SEM 25/35 radios are fitted. It can be recognized by antennae that are longer than those in use with the SEM 80/90 radios. The vehicle depicted here was in service with Pionierbataillon 1 in Holzminden. The rails on the roof provide protection for two cable reels that are stored there.

Raketenwerfer 110 mm from Selbstfahrlafette 2, 2.Batterie, Raketenartilleriebataillon 12, 1.Panzerdivision, September 1993
This vehicle sports the regular camouflage pattern of green (bronzegrün RAL 6031), brown (lederbraun RAL 8027) and black (teerschwarz RAL 9021). The call sign "2C" in black denotes the third launcher of the second battery. The name "Fortuna", the famous Roman Goddess of luck, has been applied in black to both sides of the launcher.

Flugabwehrraketenfahrzeug 1 Roland, Horstgruppe, Marinefliegergeschwader 2, Eggebeck, August 1996
Painted in the regular camouflage pattern, this vehicle is one of twenty FFRs based on the MAN 15 t milgl A1 br, which is in current service with the German Navy. The one shown here is in service with the air defense element of Eggebeck air base, home of Naval Aviation Wing 2. The inscription "Marine", or Navy, has been applied in gray (fehgrau RAL 7000) on both sides of the shelter.

Transportpanzer 1 Fuchs A4 (R stsatz MILAN), 2.Kompanie, Gepanzerter Einsatzverband, GCONSFOR, Rakovica, Bosnia and Herzegovina, August 1998

This up-armored TPz-1 A4, which is fitted with the MILAN ATGW installation kit, was seen during a patrol on the way to Kiseljak. It belongs to 2nd Company, Armored Task Force, German contingent of the Stabilization Force. The regular SFOR badge has been applied to the vehicle's sides, with lettering in Latin and Cyrillic. A German flag flies from one of the antennae, while a blue/white pennant is attached to the other.

Sp hpanzer 2 Luchs A2, 2.Kompanie, Gepanzerter Einsatzverband, GCONSFOR, Kiseljak, Bosnia and Herzegovina, August 1998

This SpPz 2 A2 has the call sign "Tiger 2/5", denoting the 5th platoon, 2nd Company of the Armored Task Force. Apart from the SFOR badge, seen below the rearward driver's station, the vehicle sports an arrow pointing upward as the official coalition marking. A wooden box, known as the Rommelkiste, has been added to the rear engine deck. The top cover is painted orange for air recognition purposes. This is used as extra stowage space for personal gear.

This command and control version TPz-1 A4 Fü/Fu of 2nd Company, Panzeraufklärungsbataillon 2 (Armored Reconnaissance Battalion 2) was captured on film carrying out a reconnaissance mission during an exercise in Bergen in 1989. The towing cable is in the required position for amphibious operations.

This TPz-1 A4 Fü/Fu represents a tank, as denoted by the yellow triangle applied during the Reforger 1991 exercise "Certain Shield". The crew on board are tankers. Note the exhaust pipe running along the left side of the vehicle.

With the 7.62 mm MG 3 A1 machine gun at the ready, the tow cable in position, and the covers on the side windows closed, this TPz-1 A4 Fü/Fu of Panzerpionierkompanie 10 makes its way across the river Weser near Holzminden during an exercise in 1991.

A TPz-1 A4 Fü/Fu on an exercise with 12th (GE) Panzerdivision in 1991. The white cross on the bow denotes a neutral vehicle. The Fuchs has a Mercedes Benz LS7FS power-assisted circulating ball-and-nut steering system, which operates on the first and second axles.

The fuel filler cap on the right side of this TPz-1 A4 Fü/Fu has just been opened, and the vehicle will soon be refilled with diesel fuel. The photo was taken during the joint Dutch/German exercise "Light Viper" in 1993.

A completely white TPz-1 A4 Fü/Fu command and control vehicle is loaded aboard a train after returning from the UN mission in Somalia in early 1993. The extendible mast, which would be tilted upward into an attached holder on the frame for operation, is seen in its stored position on the rear right side of the vehicle.

The commander of an up-armored TPz-1 Fuchs aims the vehicle's 7.62 mm MG 3 A1 machine gun while on patrol in early 1997. The up-armored Fuchs also received additional armor on the hatches. The armor around the machine gun was added at a later stage. The SFOR badge is carried by all German vehicles in service in the former Yugoslavia.

The up-armored version of the TPz-1 A4 Fü/Fu sees service among the German contingent of the Stabilization Forces (SFOR) in Bosnia and Herzegovina. Although it lacks the red and white warning plates commonly seen on up-armored vehicles, it can be recognized by the slightly offset license plate on the bow.

The specially built communication and control version of the Fuchs can be recognized by the 5 kW auxiliary power unit (APU) located in the rear left door. When equipped with the SEM 25/35, it is known as the TPz-1 A2 Führung/Funk. When the SEM 80/90 radios are installed, it is designated the TPz-1 A5 Führung/Funk. An example of the latter was seen during an exercise of Panzerbrigade 36, 12th (GE) Panzerdivision.

This is the TPz-1 A5 Fü/Fu used by the brigade commander of Panzerbrigade 34, 12th (GE) Panzerdivision during an exercise in 1991. The communication/control version of the Fuchs is equipped with appropriate communication equipment for higher level assignment, a telescopic mast for static operation, plus foldable seats and tables, as well as a SEA 5 kW auxiliary power unit installed in the rear left door.

Here is a closer look at the housing of the SEA 5 kW (APU) installed in the left rear door of a TPz-1 A5 Fü/Fu. The door is fully functional. The APU is the only external recognition feature that distinguishes it from the TPz-1 A4 Fü/Fu. The internal layout of the vehicle could differ depending on the mission it is assigned to. Of the 265 TPz-1 command and control vehicles built, 134 are used by air defense units (Gepard and Roland). The vehicle depicted here, which belongs to Panzerbrigade 18, 7th (GE) Panzerdivision, is seen during the exercise "Offenes Visier".

This TPz-1 A5 Führung/Funk communication vehicle is part of Panzerbrigade 3, 1st (GE) Panzerdivision. It is shown during an exercise in Bergen in August 1989. According to the white crosses applied to it, the vehicle was used by neutral forces.

A TPz-1 A5 Fü/Fu of Panzeraufklärungsbataillon 5 in Sontra plays a part in the training of soldiers in preparation of their service among IFOR in Croatia and Bosnia.

The extendible antenna of this TPz-1 A5 Fü/Fu is shown in its operational mode. It is used in static operation only and enhances the range for the radios.

The TPz-1 A2 PARA also has a SAE 5 kW auxiliary power unit installed in the rear left door. The red crosses of this vehicle of Panzeraufklärungsbataillon 12 denote that it was part of the opposing forces.

A Transportpanzer 1 Fuchs A2 PARA (Panzer-Aufklärungs-Radar) with the RASIT battlefield surveillance radar. The radar can be hydraulically raised up to 1.8 meters (6 feet) and is lowered into the vehicle when not in operation. The vehicle shown here is seen during an exercise of Panzeraufklärungsbataillon 12 in 1989.

When the SEM 80/90 radios are fitted to it, the vehicle with the RASIT radar is designated as TPz-1 A4 PARA. Altogether, 110 vehicles of this version have been built and are seeing service with the armored reconnaissance battalions on a divisional level, with nine per battalion. This TPz-1 A4 PARA here is in operation, with all hatches and covers closed. The RASIT radar can be operated by remote control by a 30-meter (33-yard) long cable, which is stowed at the rear right side of the vehicle.

A look inside the TPz-1 A 4 PARA radar vehicle shows the SEM 80/90 radios installed to the left and the radar operator's seat to the right.

A close-up of the French-designed RASIT (radar sur terre intermédiaire) DR-PT 2a battlefield surveillance radar of a TPz-1 A4 PARA. A hinged circular cover, which swings open to the left, provides protection for the radar system after it is lowered into the troop compartment when not in use. The RASIT DR-PT 2a battlefield surveillance radar, which is hydraulically raised to a height of up to 1.8 meters (6 feet) for operation, has a range of approximately 20 km (12.4 miles).

The subject of this photo is a Transportpanzer 1 Fuchs A6 ABC, the NBC reconnaissance version. It is equipped with devices for radiation and contamination detection and sampling and marking in proposed contaminated areas. The NBC-detection equipment includes radiation and chemical agent detector units and sampling instruments as part of the MM-1 system, as well as yellow marker flags. All operations are carried out under full NBC protection from within the vehicle.

A rear view of a TPz-1 A6 ABC, the NBC reconnaissance version of the TPz-1 Fuchs. The work opening with the attached special glove can be seen in the lower part of the rear door. The barely visible small box contains yellow marker flags.

The two-wheeled probes seen at the lower left of the vehicle's rear are used to register settled warfare agents while the vehicle is on the move. The NBC sampling system, which is seen in action here, consists of the sampling device and the sampling gripper for picking up and transporting samples. With the use of a special glove, samples are taken through the work opening in the rear of the vehicle.

A TPz-1 A6 ABC participates in an exercise recently held at the German Armor School in Munster. The vehicle is equipped with the FOA 25 vehicle navigation system.

The wheeled probes of a TPz-1 A6 ABC of Pionierbrigade 20 are deployed during a reconnaissance mission. The ambient air to be analyzed is used as the carrier gas for the detection probe. This gas carries the combat agent, which evaporates on contact with the probe surface, to the MM-1 spectro analyzer through a probe lead, which simultaneously acts as the separation system. The wheels of both probes have silicone tires and are used to register settled warfare agents while the vehicle is moving.

After the reconnaissance mission, the TPz-1 A6 ABC must be decontaminated by a special procedure that includes a wash with solvent "soap" and a lot of water. The NBC-Fox is also known as the ABC-Spürfuchs in German service.

Another TPz-1 A6 ABC, the NBC reconnaissance version of the Fuchs, is seen here in service with the German contingent of SFOR in Bosnia.

A TPz-1 A6 ABC in service with the German SFOR contingent, seen here at the Rajlovac camp, a former military airfield of the Yugoslavian Air Force. The soldier wears NBC protective clothing during training. According to undisclosed sources, some suspicious ampules were littering the area of the former Yugoslavian airfield and had to be very carefully removed.

A heavily camouflaged improved TPz-1 A6 ABC of Pionierbrigade 20 takes part in an exercise in April 1998. The meteorological probe can be clearly seen on the right side of the vehicle.

This product-improved TPz-1 A6 ABC is equipped with a GPS navigation system and a meteorological probe. This particular vehicle is one of the first vehicles so modified. It is shown during an exercise of Pionierbrigade 20, 1st (GE) Panzerdivision in April 1998. The vehicle has chains over the wheels to enhance cross-country capability on muddy ground. Approximately one third of the NBC-Foxes will be improved to this standard.

In 1991 the US Army received sixty NBC-Foxes, as they are called, directly from German stocks for use in support of Operation "Desert Storm". They were modified with a US-type smoke mortar (of British origin), an alternate machine gun mount, US radios, and an air conditioner. Here an M93 NBC-Fox belonging to the 3rd Infantry Division takes part in an exercise at the CMTC Hohenfels following Desert Storm. A small armored box on the right rear of the vehicle, which contains a transceiver for the crew's intercom, was also added to the M93.

Here we see an M93 NBC-Fox NBCRS of the 11th Armored Cavalry Regiment, which saw service during the Gulf War. The vehicle has its trim vane erected.

33

A product-improved TPz-1 A6 ABC of ABC-Abwehrbataillon 7, 7th (GE) Panzerdivision in operation during exercise "Strong Resolve" in March 1998. The event was held about 100 km (62 miles) north of Narvik in Norway. (Carl Schulze)

The electronic warfare version of the TPz-1 is designated the Transportpanzer 1 Hummel (Bumble Bee) A1. Shown here is the version with the EK 33 jammer kit, which works in the range HF (1.6 - 30 MHz), VHF (20 - 68/150 MHz), and UHF (100 - 500 MHz) with an output of 2 kW. A SEA 15 kW auxiliary power unit has been installed behind the engine compartment, and a cooling system has been built into the left rear door.

Since the TPz-1 A1 has no amphibious capabilities, it has no trim vane on the bow and no propellers at the rear. The two examples shown, which belong to 1st (GE) Panzerdivision, are part of an exercise in Bergen in late 1989.

Two TPz-1 Hummel A1 vehicles in operation during an exercise in Bergen. Both vehicles are marked as neutral by white crosses. The rear end of the electronic warfare version, the Hummel, differs from that of the Fuchs by having no propellers and no trim vane.

The exhaust pipe of the built-in SAE 15 kW auxiliary power unit of the TPz-1 A1 can be seen next to the smoke mortar array. On this version, there is only one large hatch in the roof.

A TPz-1 Hummel A1 on a rather bumpy test course at Trier WTD 41 proving grounds. This vehicle has not yet been fitted with antennae fitted for the EK 33 jammer kit.

The Royal Dutch Army operates 18 of the TPz-1 A1 electronic warfare version of the vehicle. Note that it has an alternate machine gun mount and Philips-built radios, but retains the German-built smoke mortars. This particular vehicle is seen during exercise "Light Viper" in 1993. The red and white warning signs are only carried on public roads.

The second version of the TPz-1 Hummel A1 is equipped with a VHF detection system made by AEG-Telefunken. The detection system is mounted on a foldable mast, which can be erected to a height of up to 6 meters (6. yards). The photo shows a Dutch vehicle during exercise "Light Viper". Its VHF detection system is stowed in the folded down position. Note that it lacks the APU/cooling device in the rear left door.

A TPz-1 A1 electronic warfare vehicle of the British Army that has safely returned from the war in the Gulf. The vehicle came from German stocks, but additional racks for water cans were added to the upper bow and to the sides of the vehicle. The British Army also made use of the NBC-Fox. (Andreas Kirchhoff)

A TPz-1 A1, equipped with prototype of the HELAS passive electronic radar reconnaissance system, seen here in the folded down position. The vehicle is fitted with early-style tires.

The HELAS prototype, developed by Siemens, with the sensor raised into vertical position for operation. The system is able to detect electromagnetic radiation from radar and fire control systems, as well as localized signal processing. (Sabine Rotter)

Here the prototype of the HELAS passive electronic radar is fully raised. It is mounted on a TPz-1 Hummel A1.

A TPz-1 Fuchs A4 as offered by Thyssen Henschel to the German Air Force for explosive ordnance disposal (EOD) service. It mounts a TS-15 turret with 20 mm gun and a coaxial 7.62 mm MG 3 machine gun. (Sabine Rotter)

The necessary EOD modifications to a basic TPz-1 include the following: reinforcement of the frontal armor; minor modifications of the hull to take the TS-15 Rheinmetall turret; omission of the smoke mortars and lateral vision blocks of the crew compartment; omission of the water propulsion; and internal modifications to accept the EOD operational kit.

Following an air attack, sensor controlled mines and bombs eventually affect ground operation on an air base. EOR/EOD operations help to restore operational readiness. The stand-off mode is an effective measure developed by the German Air Force whereby the bombs and mines are destroyed simply by firing at them. For night operation, a Xenon searchlight would be attached to the turret of the TPz-1 Fuchs A4.

An 8 x 8 version of the Transportpanzer was developed, but it never entered service. It was planned to be fitted with a turret, mounting a 25 mm gun. The prototype vehicle shown here is currently stored at WTD 41 in Trier.

A French-built VBL offered by Panhard/MaK underwent comparative trials with the GST Zobel (Sable) during the light reconnaissance vehicle development program in 1989. (MaK Systemgesellschaft)

The GST-built Zobel light-armored 4 x 4 amphibious reconnaissance vehicle features a low-cost hull construction that provides all-around protection against light ammunition. It has complete interior NBC protection. Two propellers on the bow provide water propulsion. The vehicle would have a three-man crew consisting of the commander, driver and radio operator.

The Zobel has four-wheel steering, and each wheel station has an independent hydropneumatic suspension (McPherson). It does not have a tire inflation system, but the CTS developed by Continental tire company enables the vehicle to operate even on flattened tires. The vehicle is powered by a Daimler Benz OM 603 turbo-charged diesel engine, developing 105 kW at 4,600 rpm and allowing a maximum speed 120 km/h (75 mph) on roads. Its combat weight would be around 5 tonnes (5.5 tons).

The Zobel would be armed with a 40 mm automatic grenade launcher and would carry an integrated infra-red vision system. The Zobel served as a platform for the development of the Fennek 4 x 4 light reconnaissance vehicle.

The Fennek (Desert Fox) reconnaissance vehicle is a joint development of DAF Special Products and Krauss Maffei-Wegmann. The first four pre-series vehicles have been intensively tested, two by the Dutch and two by the German Armed Forces. The elevating platform, with various reconnaissance equipment such as CCD day vision camera, thermal imager and laser rangefinder, is shown here in the raised position. For remote controlled operation, the sensor head can also be attached to a tripod away from the vehicle. (Wegmann)

The Fennek has a tire inflation system and a ground clearance of 40 cm (16 inches). Its crew of three can operate for five days on independent reconnaissance patrols. An auxiliary power unit has been built in, as well as an NBC protection system and a GPS navigation system. The armament consists of a 40 mm automatic grenade launcher. (Wegmann)

The Fennek is protected against small arms fire, and the IR signature was minimized due to a special exhaust ducting. The engine has an output of 177 kW (241 PS) and allows a maximum speed of 115 km/h (71 mph) on roads. The range is approximately 860 km (534 miles) on roads and 400 km (248 miles) cross-country. According to plans, 336 Fennek light reconnaissance vehicles will eventually replace the Spähpanzer 2 Luchs A2. (Wegmann)

The first Spähpanzer 2 Luchs was delivered to the Bundeswehr in September 1975. With the installation of the SEM 80/90 radios, its designation was changed to SpPz 2 Luchs A1. Starting in 1985, the Luchs was modified with a thermal observation and gunnery sight, which led to the designation SpPz 2 Luchs A2. In this close-up of the right side of the turret, the armored housing of the thermal sight is shown to good advantage, as are the smoke mortars.

The SpPz 2 Luchs served in the armored reconnaissance battalions on divisional level. These two Luchs A2 of Panzeraufklärungsbataillon 3 were put out of action for four hours during exercise "Offenes Visier" in 1989.

A SpPz 2 A2 of Panzeraufkluärungsbataillon 2 undergoes maintenance while on exercise in Bergen in 1989.

The Luchs has an oversized width according to German traffic law, so it has to carry red and white warning plates, along with the obligatory warning light ("whoopie light"), while traveling on public roads.

Until recently the reconnaissance battalion of a division was equipped with the Leopard 1 A5 and SpPz 2 Luchs A2 as the major weapon systems. Seen here is such a duo during an exercise in Munster in 1990.

At slow speed, the SpPz 2 A2 can make use of the optional all-wheel steering, as demonstrated by this vehicle from Panzeraufkluärungsbataillon L 11 during an exercise in late 1990.

41

The Luchs has a special rearward driver (and Morse radio operator, for long range), which enables the vehicle to drive in both directions at the same maximum speed. A headlight, which is installed above the license plate in a niche, is seen here covered up. The vehicle retains the two SRP 010 propellers at the rear, although the vehicle is no longer cleared for amphibious operations.

The main armament of the Luchs consists of a 20 mm Rh 202 machine cannon mounted in a TS-7 two man turret. A 7.62 mm machine gun on skate/ring mount is provided as secondary armament; it is operated by the commander. The cannon is dual fed, and the ammunition provided consists of 300 rounds of high explosive (HE) and 75 armor piercing rounds (AP). The spent casings are ejected to the right side through the circular housing seen to the right of the national insignia. The vehicles shown lined up here belong to the German Armor School in Munster. They are fitted with early tread-pattern wheels.

At a speed of up to 30 km/h (19 mph), the forward and the rearward driver of the Luchs can make use of the all-wheel steering. When driving at higher speed, the steering system for the rear axle pair is locked, and the front pair is locked when driving rearward. The turning radius with front-wheel steering is 9.7 m (32 feet), and 5.8 m (19 feet) with all-wheel steering. Note the large entrance door installed between the two axle pairs on the left side of the vehicle.

The SpPz 2 A2 has a combat weight of 19,800 kg (43,560 lb.) and tires in the dimensions of 14.00-20. The hull, which is made of all-welded steel, offers protection from small arms fire and artillery shrapnel. Over its frontal arc, the armor offers full protection from 20 mm projectiles. The one shown here, which is part of Panzeraufklärungsbataillon 1, carries the tactical number "311", visible below the tow bar attached to the vehicle's left side.

The Luchs is powered by a Daimler Benz OM 403 V-10 cylinder turbo-charged multi-fuel engine, developing 389 PS (287 kW) at 2,500 rpm, normally operated with diesel fuel (NATO designation F 54), developing 287 kW (389 PS). The fuel tanks have a capacity of 500 liters (132 gallons), giving a maximum range of approximately 700 km (435 miles). The maximum achievable speed is 90 km/h (56 mph), in either forward or reverse drive.

The Luchs is able to cross narrow water obstacles only. When introduced into service, the vehicle was fully amphibious, propelled in the water by two steerable Schottel propellers attached to the rear. Due to the weight added when the vehicle was modernized, it lost this capability.

A Spähpanzer 2 Luchs A2 and a Transportpanzer 1 Fuchs A4 of Panzeraufklärungsbataillon 5 in Sontra, during the training of soldiers who would soon participate in the IFOR mission in Croatia and Bosnia. Both vehicles carry coalition markings and IFOR badges.

A SpPz 2 Luchs A2 on a very tough trial course at WTD 41 proving grounds in Trier. The suspension consists of a vertical coil spring and a hydraulic shock absorber on each wheel station. The axles have differential locks and are supported by longitudinal bars with bogies for all axles.

Under normal circumstances, a reconnaissance patrol would consist of two SpPz A2s. The vehicles would be heavily camouflaged, as seen here. The photo shows a vehicle belonging to Panzeraufklärungsbataillon 5 during a recent exercise.

A SpPz 2 Luchs A2 of Panzeraufklärungsbataillon 5 during exercises to prepare the soldiers of the battalion for their IFOR mission in the summer of 1996. German vehicles rarely carried the white IFOR inscription. Normally only the official IFOR badge was used.

In December 1996 the IFOR mandate ended and the Stabilization Force (SFOR) came into being. Seen here during an inspection patrol in March 1997, a SpPz A2 patrols along a fence surrounding a Bosnian military installation.

A SpPz 2 Luchs A2 on patrol in the town of Hadjici in April 1997. Apparently the crew has applied the names of their sweethearts next to their stations. In addition to the SEM 80/90, the Luchs is equipped with a 400 W HF Morse radio for long distance use.

Another view of the same SpPz 2 Luchs A2 seen in the previous photo on patrol in Hadjici. One of the up-armored TPz-1 Fuchs can be seen in background. Altogether, the patrol consisted of two SpPz 2 A2s and four TPz-1s. The obligatory orange air identification panel can be seen on the engine deck.

A SpPz 2 A2 in front of a destroyed hotel near the Olympic grounds on Mount Igman, near Sarajevo, in early 1997. In areas such as this, the threat posed by mines was quite intense. The vehicle depicted here has the official SFOR badge applied to its trim vane and sides, along with the coalition marking applied in silver on the lower bow.

In August 1998, a SpPz 2 A2 heads out on an SFOR patrol to Kiseljak and Sarajevo, with an up-armored TPz-1 A4 leading the way. This photo was taken from the lead vehicle.

This SpPz 2 A2, which has an additional searchlight fitted on the turret, is shown in Kiseljak near the former UN headquarters in the summer of 1998. The red and white warning plates required by German traffic law are even worn in Bosnia and Herzegovina.

After they have carried out all preparations, the crews of two SpPz 2 A2s wait to go out on patrol in August 1998. The temperature around midday was measured at 70 degrees C (158 degrees F).

Young girls wave a greeting as "Tiger 2/5" passes by on patrol on the way to Kiseljak. SFOR patrols like this one make such a peaceful scene possible.

Nowadays life has returned to most regions of Bosnia, and small market places like the one being passed by "Tiger 2/5" are a common sight again.

SFOR's "Tiger 2/5" patrols along a road in Dobrinia near Sarajevo airport. This area once suffered heavy damage as part of the front lines, not to mention the threat of danger posed by presumably tons of mines planted all over the area. From 1997 until today, all mines have been removed by locals under the supervision and support of UNHCR.

A SpPz 2 Luchs A2 on patrol in Dobrinia in August 1998 takes up a position in front of a ruined house. The vehicle is making use of the all-wheel steering, which considerably enhances its maneuverability in narrow streets. The houses have been cleared of mines and rubble, and rebuilding may begin soon.

The latest equipment installed on the Spähpanzer 2 Luchs A2 in service with the German SFOR contingent includes the GPS navigation system, along with a gyrocompass and an additional circular antenna. All are mounted on the rear engine deck.

The GPS antenna is installed at the rearward driver's station.

The tubular housing is part of the gyrocompass, which is installed at the rear right on the engine deck.

The circular antenna for the data transmitter is fitted to the rear left of the engine deck.

An 8 x 8 experimental chassis developed by Daimler Benz is able to be fitted with large turrets derived from those fitted to main battle tanks. This vehicle is known as Gepanzerter Radkampfwagen 90 (RKW 90), i.e., armored wheeled tank. It is seen here during a test drive at WTD 41 in September 1995.

The 8 x 8 prototype, which was built partially with state financing, is the experimental version of an entire family of 4 x 4, 6 x 6 and 8 x 8 armored wheeled vehicles. It has been going through testing since the middle of 1986, and may serve as a source for the development of the GTK, the replacement for the Transportpanzer 1.

CONCORD
PUBLICATIONS COMPANY

Battle on Two Fronts
1944-45

Tom Cockle

CONCORD
PUBLICATIONS COMPANY